Flip Flap rox

Written by
Cath Jones

Illustrated by
Emma Proctor

Ransom

It is a dark, dark night, when Fox first creeps from her den in the wood.

"Mum," whispers a little fox. "Bring back some food for me!"

Pad, pad, pad. Fox's paws are firm on the damp soil.

Down the hill she trots, near the silver birch trees and the deep, deep pond.

Then Fox sits down on Mrs Smith's well-kept lawn.

Sniff, sniff, sniff. Fox can smell food!

Look, Mrs Smith has a cat flap for her kitten.

Flip flap. Fox creeps up to the cat flap and nips in.

With a lick and a crunch, Fox has the little kitten's supper. Not one little bit is left.

Then, pad, pad, pad. Flip flap.

Fox nips back into the garden.

Where is Fox going now?

Fox is setting off to hunt for food for her cub.

Fox visits Mr Blue. Mr Blue has a cat flap too. It is for his big, fat cat, Whiskers.

Flip flap. Fox creeps in and has Whiskers' supper! Not one little bit is left.

Look at Fox now. What a big tum and what a big yawn!

Now Fox needs a little nap! She spots a drawer ajar and creeps into it.

But now Mrs Smith is back – and so is
Mr Blue. They meet on the lawn and chat.

Kitten and Whiskers are sad.
They have had no food!

What has been happening? Mr Blue and
Mrs Smith set off to hunt for clues.

They spot little bits of dirt on the cat flap
and lots of paw prints!

What big clues!

Deep in the drawer, Fox hears Mr Blue and Mrs Smith.

She sits as still as a statue.

Pad, pad, pad. Fox jumps from the drawer. She trots across the bedroom and creeps down the stairs.

Mr Blue and Mrs Smith do not spot her.

Flip.

Fox pats the cat flap.

But now her tum is too big. She has had too much food and she is too big for the cat flap.

What will she do now?

13

Then Mr Blue and Mrs Smith spot Fox near the cat flap!

They stand next to Fox and clap and yell. "Go back to the woods, little fox! Shoo!"

But Fox still needs food for her cub.

So, as she runs, she grabs Mr Blue's chicken supper!

Pad, pad, pad. Back to the wood she trots, back to her den, back to her cub.

"Yum," whispers the little fox cub, deep in the den. "Thank you, Mum, for my chicken supper!"